MW00807985

The Score Is Tied in the Bottom of the Ninth Inning!

With one out, Bruce Marshall singles and you make two moves. The first one is easy. Walter Lopez is the fastest man on the bench, so you put him in to pinch-run for Marshall. The next move is more difficult. It's the pitcher's turn to bat and you have to choose a pinch hitter. Who can do the job and win the game?

If you put up Albert Edwards, turn to page 36.

If you let Terrence Brown pinch-hit, turn to page 44.

REMEMBER—A WORLD SERIES VICTORY DEPENDS ON YOUR DECISIONS!

PLAY-IT-YOUR-WAY SPORTS BOOKS for you to enjoy

A Play-It-Your-Way
Sports Book #3

WORLD SERIES PRESSURE

Mitch Gelman

Illustrated by Al Fiorentino

AN ARCHWAY PAPERBACK
Published by POCKET BOOKS • NEW YORK

AN ARCHWAY PAPERBACK *Original*

 An Archway Paperback published by
POCKET BOOKS, a division of Simon & Schuster, Inc.
1230 Avenue of the Americas, New York, N.Y. 10020

ISBN: 0-671-47577-0

First Archway Paperback printing April, 1984

10 9 8 7 6 5 4 3 2 1

AN ARCHWAY PAPERBACK and colophon are trademarks
of Simon & Schuster, Inc.

WHICH WAY is a registered trademark
of Simon & Schuster, Inc.

PLAY IT YOUR WAY is a trademark
of Simon & Schuster, Inc.

Printed in the U.S.A.

IL 4+

For Uncle Abe, and Ben,
two men who have had
a strong influence
on my decisions

ATTENTION!

Play-It-Your-Way Sports Books must be read in a special way. DO NOT READ THE PAGES IN ORDER. If you do, the story will make no sense at all. Instead, follow the directions at the bottom of each page until you come to an ending. Only then should you return to the beginning and start all over again, making different choices this time.

There are many possibilities for exciting baseball action. Some choices will lead your team to victory. Some choices will bring your team defeat. There are 26 different endings to this book—12 victories, 12 defeats, and two surprises. Go back to the beginning as often as you like and try again. See how many times you can win.

Play alone or with a friend. And remember: follow the directions carefully. Good luck. Have fun!

What a tremendous victory! You surprised everybody by winning the pennant. All the experts—coaches, sportswriters, fans—said the Bombers had no chance. But the "experts" were wrong.

For three years in a row, the Bombers finished in last place. Then, this season, they hired you as their manager. And after an exciting win in the National League play-offs, here they are, fighting for the championship in the final game of the World Series.

Your players have shown they have the talent to win it. They have risen to World Series pressure and battled the American League champs, the Terrible Terriers, down to the wire. Rocket-powered second baseman Jet Johnson has been stealing bases like the old cowboy outlaw, Jesse James, knocked off trains. Old slugger Lou Robinson has been great at bat and at first base. And 22-year-old phenom Jerry Crane has pitched two shutouts.

(continued on page 2)

It has come down to the final game of the best-of-seven Series, tied at three games each. This afternoon's game is the biggest of your career. All your life, you've wanted to be the best at something. Win today and that World Series diamond ring goes on your finger. And it tells the universe: "I am the best. Numero Uno." That is what today is all about. The pride in proving you are Number One.

From the bottom step of the dugout, you glance at your Bombers taking infield practice. Your mind wanders back over a season of success. A season marked by bold baseball.

Bunt. Steal. Squeeze. Take the extra base. Slide hard to break up double plays. Dive for every ground ball you can possibly knock down. Get that uniform dirty. Chatter in the infield, cheer on the bench. Scratch out those runs and make them stand up with tight defense and tough pitching.

Concentration. Cooperation. Hustle. You expect those qualities from your ball club, nicknamed "The Clawing Cats" for the paw-and-claw style of play they displayed all year.

Win the Series and the Clawing Cats dine on fresh tuna and champagne. Lose and it's week-old Kal Kan and sour milk.

(continued on page 3)

You look out at infield practice, and you can taste victory. Adrenaline is flowing in cups, quarts, gallons. Energy is High Voltage Danger!

The Jet and shortstop Slick Desmond are turning smooth, quick double plays. The Jet is always solid, but you hope Slick, an undependable fielder, can play tough today. He runs, hits, and hustles, but his wild throw in Game Four cost you the game.

Too bad. Because slugger Lou had just hit his second home run of the Series to put the Bombers ahead in the top of the ninth. If Lou hits another home run today, this season will mark a personal milestone: 37 homers at the age of 37.

In right field, Skeets Rodriguez loosens up his cannon arm. Skeets has thrown out two runners already this Series. Power-hitting Moose Harrington has been steady in left field. And center fielder Eddie Cooper has recovered from the hamstring he pulled in the play-offs.

Over at third, Billy Sawatski seems to be going good.

It's mainly Bruce Marshall, your catcher, whom you are concerned about. All season, he was your clutch hitter and team leader. Then he went into a slump for the play-offs and the first couple of Series

(continued on page 4)

games. After Game Three, he finally admitted what was causing his problems at the plate. He has a hairline fracture of the left thumb. A foam pad protected the thumb on defense, but the injury caused great pain and difficulty while swinging the bat. Marshall's substitute, Albert Edwards, did a decent job in Games Four, Five, and Six, but you are going with Marshall today. Sure hope his hand holds up.

(continued on page 5)

Your opponents, the Terriers, have won five World Series in a row. If they win today, they break the New York Yankees' consecutive World Series victory record, set from 1949 through 1953, and will be known as the best ball club ever. You can imagine how much they want it.

Terrier right fielder Hank Percy compares himself to Babe Ruth and has a personalized license plate which says SULTAN. Victory today means a lot to him and to the Terriers' starting pitcher, six-million-dollar free agent Rex Tobler, who wants to show he is worth all that money.

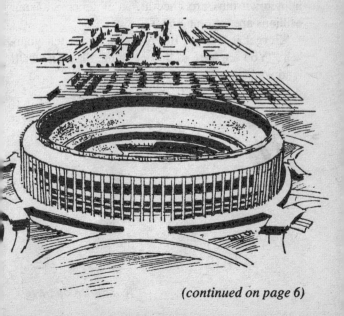

(continued on page 6)

Their all-star shortstop, Tony Mason, also is a dogged competitor. He stole home to beat you last night. Today's game is going to be tough.

You can barely hear the NBC sportscaster who is trying to interview you over the roar of the crowd. A fan in a furry cat costume has jumped on top of your dugout. It's CATMAN. He is snarling and gnashing huge cat claws at the Terriers' side of the field. The fans love it. "Claw, Cats, Claw!" they chant. "Claw, Cats, Claw!"

The pressure mounts. The president of the USA is in the commissioner's box. More than 60,000 hometown fans are cheering in Bomber Stadium. Millions are watching on TV.

"Forget it. Forget the pressure," you tell yourself. "You are here to do one thing. Play Clawball! And win."

(continued on page 7)

You still have to decide who will be your starting pitcher. Your top three pitchers—Spud Roselli, Jerry Crane, and Jackson Barnes—have been working on a three-day rotation during the Series. Normally, today would be Roselli's turn. But he has been clobbered the last two times he's pitched. He lost 8–3 in the opener and was knocked out early in Game Four. Barnes is out because he threw seven innings yesterday. Crane has had two days' rest. In his two Series appearances, he shut out the Terriers both times. Both Crane and Roselli are warming up.

It is time to bring out the lineup card:

> Jet Johnson, second base
> Skeets Rodriguez, right field
> Lou Robinson, first base
> Moose Harrington, left field
> Billy Sawatski, third base
> Slick Desmond, shortstop
> Eddie Cooper, center field
> Bruce Marshall, catcher

Who is your pitcher? Is it tired but spectacular Jerry Crane? Or have you chosen to give Spud Roselli another chance?

—If you want Crane to start, turn to page 8.

—If you want Roselli to start, turn to page 10.

This is it. Last chance. There is no tomorrow. It's got to be Crane. He will be able to rest all winter.

Even if Crane tires after three or four innings, at least you will have had your ace in there for a while. He is only 22 years old, but he has poise. A year ago, he was pitching Class-A rookie ball out on the farm. Now he is pitching in Game Seven under World Series pressure. The crowd explodes when they see Jerry Crane trot in from the Bomber bull pen. Usually your pitchers ride in, perched in the bull-pen car—the Catmobile. Today, no one can sit down. They are all up for the biggest game of the season.

The electric scoreboard flashes "Claw, Crane, Claw!" The pitcher responds. He mows down the Terriers, striking out their number three hitter, Hank Percy, on a sidearm slider to retire the side. "My paw pitch, Coach. You see it?" yells Crane as he bounds into the dugout. You slap him on the back. "Keep clawing, kid," you say.

(continued on page 9)

Now you have to get some runs. Your pitcher may have good stuff, but the Terriers have the best in the game throwing for them. They gave Rex Tobler a six-year, six-million-dollar contract when they signed him after the free-agent draft last year. You often get upset that your owner, Angry Artie Nash, is too cheap to spend big bucks on free agents. Six million was a lot of money for a pitcher. But so far, Tobler has been worth every penny to the Terriers.

Jet Johnson, your leadoff hitter, is about to step into the on-deck circle to watch Tobler throw his warm-ups. It might be a good idea to catch the Terriers off guard. Tobler is tough to hit; maybe Jet ought to try to sneak in a leadoff bunt.

"Jet," you call from the end of the dugout near the water cooler where you usually stand during games. He jogs over to you, flipping his bat up and down with his left hand.

—*If you tell Jet to bunt, turn to page 12.*

—*If you tell Jet to take his rip, turn to page 15.*

Crane is the type of pitcher who needs a lot of rest. After only two days, his arm is bound to be tired, and there is no sense in trying to win a World Series on a tired arm. Especially not against a good hitting team like the Terriers. Besides, Roselli pitched well all season. Anyone can have a couple of poor outings—and if you do not start Spud Roselli today, you risk ruining his confidence forever. May as well see what Roselli can do; you can always bring Crane in later.

Leading off for the Terriers is their superstar shortstop, Tony Mason. In Game Four, Mason tagged Roselli for three hits. This time, Spud throws inside, and Mason taps the ball back to the mound.

A big smile comes across Roselli's face as he tosses the ball to first. His confidence is back, and he gets the next Terrier batter out. Batting third for the Terriers is their top power hitter, Hank Percy.

Percy is a big left-handed hitter with a big swing. He led the American League in home runs and RBIs this season and most of his power is to right field.

(continued on page 11)

Last night, you were thinking about how to take away Percy's power. You have tried pitching him low, high, inside, outside—and have had no luck. He still pulls the ball. Then, you thought about the possibility of calling a defensive shift whenever Percy comes to bat. Your outfielders would shift toward right field; your second baseman would move toward first; your shortstop would position himself behind the bag at second; and your third baseman would move into the shortstop position. Somewhat like the shift one team used to put on when Ted Williams would come to bat.

A shift like this can take base hits away from a pull hitter. It can also leave you vulnerable if the hitter has good enough bat control to hit to the opposite field.

—*To shift on Percy, turn to page 54.*

—*To play him straightaway, turn to page 52.*

Jet Johnson is a great team player. He will do anything to win a ball game. But as soon as you tell him to bunt, his enthusiasm dies. You've never seen the Jet like that. He really wanted to hit. But you think a bunt is the best strategy, and you are the manager.

Tobler delivers a fastball, low and inside. Jet drops his bat to his waist, pivots, bends his knees, and nicks the ball.

The ball bounces on the plate as Jet races from the batter's box.

(continued on page 13)

The home-plate umpire yells, "Yerrr out! Ball hit the batter."

"What!" you scream from the dugout and tear out toward the plate. You want an explanation.

"The batter bumped into the ball after he left the batter's box. The batter is out," the umpire tells you.

There is no way Jet was out of the box that quickly. No way. You want to yell at the umpire, tell him that he is blind, that he couldn't pin a tail on a donkey if he used binoculars in broad daylight. But you don't want to get thrown out of the game.

(continued on page 14)

CATMAN leaps onto the Bomber dugout. He leads the fans in a chant: "Bad Call. Bad Call. Bad Call."

Then you cannot believe what is happening. CATMAN races onto the field, not to playfully taunt an opposing player or do his act where he stumbles into the umpire like a blind man. There is rage in CATMAN's whiskers. He is racing right at the home-plate umpire.

He leaps at the umpire, gnashing and pawing at the umpire's face and eyes. The police come running onto the field. The Terriers' catcher grabs CATMAN and drags him away.

It is too late. The umpire is all scratched up. There is blood running from his cheeks and nose.

The Bombers' team doctor takes the umpire to the hospital. Rather than play with a substitute umpire, the commissioner decides to postpone the game.

The CATMAN went crazy; now he's off to jail. And you are going back to the locker room to wait until tomorrow.

The End

You see the way Jet is swinging the bat with his left wrist. He is twitching, itching to get up there and take a cut at Tobler. If Jet gets a hit early, it will give everybody confidence.

"Jet, I have been telling the press all year that you're worth ten million Rex Toblers. Go out there and give the rich kid a licking," you say.

"Gonna drive it, Coach. Smack one," Jet says.

You can see the confidence and determination in the Jet as he grips the bat tighter and tighter. You can see the concentration in his eyes.

First pitch. Rip! Jet tears a low line drive between short and third. Base hit.

Man on first. Skeets Rodriguez is up. Skeets may have the best bat control in the league. Do you want Skeets to hit and run or swing away normally?

—*If you want Skeets to hit and run, turn to page 16.*

—*If you want Skeets to swing away, turn to page 18.*

Aggressive baseball and intelligent managing are what have taken you this far. No reason to get timid now.

You flash the sign for hit and run. As Tobler fires to the plate, Jet takes off for second. The second baseman races over to cover on the steal, leaving a big gap between first and second base. Skeets waits on a curve ball and slaps it to the opposite field for a base hit.

(continued on page 17)

Jet races toward third. The Terrier right fielder, Hank Percy, fires to third base. But he can't get the Jet. Skeets goes to second on the throw. Next up, slugger Lou Robinson singles to drive in two runs.

That is all for Tobler. Terrier manager Arthur London has seen enough. London brings in another pitcher, Leroy Marlin. Leroy is usually a starter, and a good one.

He gets the side out easily. But you are ahead 2–0 and everything is going right. Nobody scores in the second inning, but you threaten again in the bottom of the third.

Crane, of all people, doubles. Jet pops up. Crane scores on a Skeets Rodriguez single. Lou Robinson is the batter with one out.

You might be able to shake the Terriers up if you have Skeets attempt a steal.

—*To have Skeets steal, turn to page 20.*

—*If you want to play it safe, turn to page 23.*

Why get fancy? It paid off letting Jet just go up there and slug the ball. "Get up there, Skeets," you shout from the dugout. "Just stroke one."

Skeets digs in. He paws at the dirt in the batter's box with his left foot, cocks the bat, and stares at Tobler. Tobler's pitch is wide. A pitchout. The Terriers thought you would be up to something. But no one was going anywhere. You are matching your strengths against theirs.

Skeets takes ball two inside. Then Tobler hits the corner for a strike. Next pitch, Skeets pulls low and hard. It looks like a base hit. Jet gets a good jump off first and is on his way to second. Diving, Terrier shortstop Tony Mason stretches out horizontal to the ground and nabs the ball for a miraculous catch. He scrambles to his knees and fires to first to complete the double play.

Lou Robinson pops out and the score is 0–0 after one full inning.

(continued on page 19)

Still scoreless in the third inning, Jerry Crane is getting tired. You take him out and put in Karl Jurgenson, a good long reliever.

It is still 0–0 when Moose Harrington walks up to the plate in the bottom of the sixth. Moose is a great hulk of a man, but very mild mannered; one of the kindest men you know—except to a baseball.

The fans in the left-field bleachers love Moose. A whole section is called the Moose Pen. And members of the Moose Harrington Fan Club come to games wearing antlers.

Crack! Moose tags a fastball into the Moose Pen for a home run. You are ahead 1–0 and so happy that you could put on a pair of antlers.

In the top of the seventh, the Terriers load the bases with no outs. Do you pull the infield in to try to cut off the run at home? Or do you concede the run and play back for a double play?

—To have your infield play back, turn to page 24.

—To pull your infield in, turn to page 26.

Skeets takes a big lead off first. He dances toward second. "Back!" yells your first-base coach. And Skeets dives back to the bag just before the pickoff throw from Marlin.

Skeets leads off again. This time a little closer to the bag. Again, Marlin throws over. This time the ball hits Skeets in the helmet and ricochets into foul territory. Skeets casually jogs into second.

You have the Terriers rattled. They can't seem to do anything right. You can do no wrong. Slugger Lou gets his second base hit of the game and Rodriguez scores easily.

After four innings, you are ahead 4–0. You pinch-hit for Crane and take him out of the game. "Great going, Jerry," you tell him. "But we can't ask any more from you. You've thrown enough pitches today. You've given us the lead we need. If we can't hold this one, we don't deserve the championship."

(continued on page 21)

Karl Jurgenson goes in to pitch for you. Jurgy is a little fat around the gut, but when he puts his weight behind the ball he throws heat.

In the sixth inning, your luck changes—from good to bad. The Terriers are not hitting the ball hard, but they are getting all the breaks. A Texas-League blooper, an opposite-field double, and an error by Slick Desmond give the Terriers a run and men on first and second with one out.

You go to the mound. "Just keep the ball down," you tell Jurgy. "One out. Let's get a ground ball and turn two."

Jurgy fires the next pitch around the batter's knees. He swings. Exactly what you want. A ground ball. Oh, no! The ball scoots right between shortstop and third base for a hit. The next Terrier batter doubles, and the score is tied at four.

You bring in your short-relief man, Richard Roscoe. Roscoe gets the Bombers out of the horrible sixth inning.

(continued on page 22)

Roscoe has good stuff. His fastball is popping and his curve is breaking. But he gets into a little trouble in the top of the eighth. Tony Mason doubles, and Hank Percy comes to the plate with one out. The American League home-run and RBI leader for two seasons in a row, Percy can do big damage with his bat.

After Percy, the Terriers' number four hitter, first basemen Burly Brad Boysenberry, is up. Boysenberry got on base on an error his last time up but has not been hitting the ball well today.

The score is still tied at four. There is a man on second and one out. It might be a good idea to intentionally walk Percy and pitch to the number four hitter.

—*To intentionally walk Percy, turn to page 41.*

—*To pitch to Percy, turn to page 37.*

"We are ahead three runs early in the game and Crane is throwing well," you say to yourself. "No need to take any unnecessary risks."

No need, indeed. Lou drills a double in the right-center field gap, and Skeets speeds toward third base. Your third-base coach, Peters, waves his arms like a windmill, and Skeets turns for home and scores.

Everything is going right. The guys on the bench are slapping each other's backs. Twenty-one-year-old Kid Costello, the youngest player on the team, is leaping up and down like a yo-yo. It really seems possible. You might win the World Series.

In the bottom of the fifth, you have a comfortable four-run lead, and it is Jerry Crane's turn to bat. He has thrown a lot of pitches and is working on only two days' rest. You hate to take him out of there. But you are not sure if you want to press your luck.

—*If you take Crane out, turn to page 32.*

—*If you leave Crane in, turn to page 27.*

"Go for two! Double-play depth," you yell.

Tony Mason is the batter for the Terriers. He raps a grounder toward shortstop. Slick Desmond scoops up the ball and flips backhand to Jet Johnson coming to the bag. Jet pivots and fires across his body to Lou Robinson at first. Double play.

"Way to go. All right!" you yell.

(continued on page 25)

You conceded a run. But the Terriers would have scored two runs if your infield had been in. That ball would have gone through to the outfield.

The score remains tied in the bottom of the ninth inning. With one out, Bruce Marshall singles and you make two moves. The first one is easy. Walter Lopez is the fastest man on the bench, so you put him in to pinch-run for Marshall. The next move is more difficult. It is the pitcher's turn to bat, and you have to choose a pinch hitter.

There is Albert Edwards, who was the substitute catcher while Marshall sat out with his sore hand. Edwards did well. But you also have Terrence Brown. Terrence is an old veteran. He hasn't hit yet during the Series, but he has never had trouble coming up cold in the past.

—To put up Albert Edwards, turn to page 36.

—To let Terrence Brown pinch-hit, turn to page 44.

You draw in your infielders. You want to play tight defense and cut off the tying run at the plate.

Tony Mason is the batter for the Terriers. Yes, the same player who robbed Skeets of the hit in the first inning. This time, he gets you with his bat, grounding the ball up the middle for a base hit.

If the infield had stayed back, your shortstop or second baseman might have been able to make a play. But you will never know. Two runs score. And that is all the Terriers need to beat you 2–1, and to win the World Series.

The End

Crane hits a soft line drive, which the Terrier shortstop catches. Then Crane goes out to pitch.

In the sixth inning, before you know it, the Terriers load the bases. You go out to the mound and talk to Crane. He admits his arm is tired.

You call in Richard Roscoe. He is your best short-relief man. But this is a tough spot for any pitcher. First base is not open, so Roscoe has to come right in and throw strikes. That is never easy. With the American League home-run and RBI champ Hank Percy at bat, it is downright scary.

Roscoe comes in with a fastball.

Swat! The right fielder who thinks he is Babe Ruth does a pretty good imitation of the Babe. An upper-deck home run. A grand slam which ties the score.

The grand slam gives the Terriers all the momentum they need to go on to win 6–4. You left Crane in too long. Next time, you will not be so greedy.

The End

Sometimes you just cannot play the percentages. You have a hunch. Some people can look a guy in the eye and tell if he is telling the truth or lying. You can look a guy in the eye and tell if he is going to get a hit. You look at Lou and decide he should swing away.

The fans start a rhythmic clap as Lou approaches the plate. "Lou, Lou, Lou," they chant. CATMAN, in his whiskers, cat ears, and tail, is watching intently from the top of the Bombers' dugout. Skeets is staring in from first.

(continued on page 29)

But nowhere in the stadium is the concentration more intense than between Lou Robinson and the Terriers' pitcher, reliever Al Whitcomb. Whitcomb used to throw rocks at cats when he grew up in a small town in Kentucky. He claims that is how his arm became strong. Whitcomb has always hated cats, and he told the press before the Series that he would like nothing more than to skin a few cats now.

And he was not fooling. First pitch—a fastball right at Lou's head. Lou ducks away, but it was awfully close. Second pitch—a curve for a strike.

(continued on page 31)

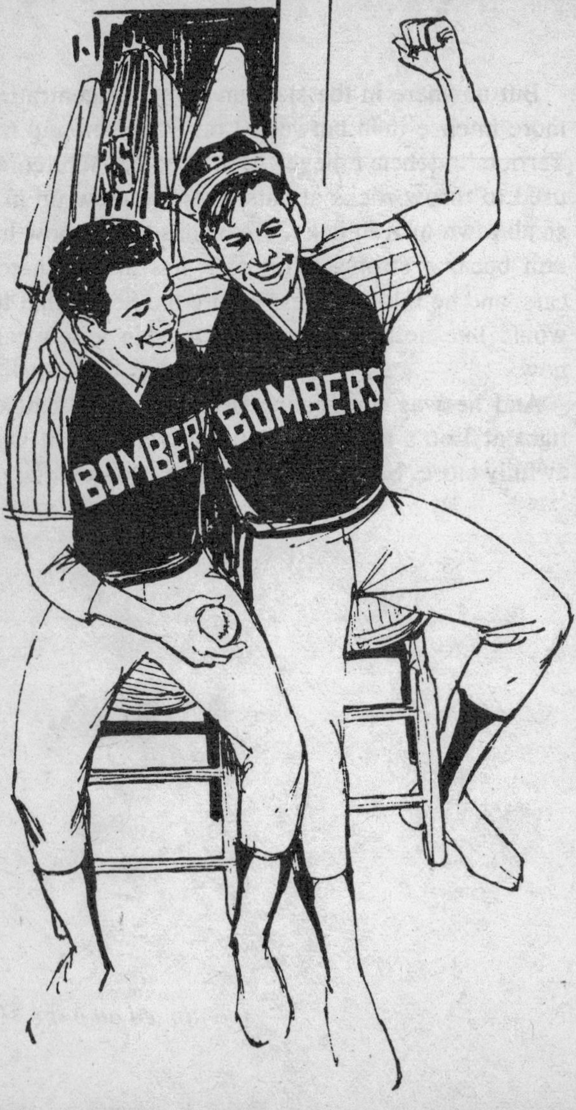
BOMBERS
BOMBERS

Lou digs in. He plants his back foot, stares at the mound. He is looking right at the point where Whitcomb releases the ball. He is not awed by any of the pitcher's antics.

Whitcomb rocks back, kicks high, and fires a fastball.

Lou strides forward and sends the pitch flying over the right-field fence.

A Robinson Rip—that is what they call those big, towering Lou Robinson home runs. He has never hit one at a better time.

As he trots around third, Lou looks out at Whitcomb, who is still standing dumbstruck on the mound. "Meow," Lou calls. "Meow." The pitcher does not hear Lou because the fans are hysterical.

This is a great win for you. Your hunch paid off. And this is a special home run for Lou. It was number 37 on the year. In the locker room, Lou is celebrating. He comes up to you. "Coach," says the man with little tufts of gray hair poking from under his cap. "Coach, thirty-seven homers for a thirty-seven-year-old makes me feel young again. When does spring training start?"

The End

"Well done, kid," you say, slapping Crane on the back. And you replace him at bat with Lawrence Silver, one of your best pinch hitters.

As soon as Silver steps out of the dugout, the fans know you have taken Crane out of the game, and they give him a standing ovation. He was remarkable this World Series. Twenty-two scoreless innings. The fans do not stop cheering until Crane comes onto the field and tips his cap.

Silver gives them something else to cheer about— a single up the middle.

(continued on page 33)

Jet singles Silver to third. With no one out, the Jet steals second and Skeets singles in two runs. You are ahead 6–0 with four more innings to play. Whom do you put in to pitch?

You still have Spud Roselli, who was supposed to start the game. You also could put in Karl Jurgenson, a long reliever.

The Terriers have made some changes since the game began. They still have switch hitter Tony Mason, the home-run-hitting lefty Hank Percy, and right-handed hitter Burly Brad Boysenberry. But they have put in two substitutes since the game began: third baseman Pete Epsy and center fielder Reggie Trowbridge. Both are left-handed hitters.

Remember, left-handed hitters usually hit right-handed pitchers better than they hit left-handed pitchers.

Do you want to bring in your left-hander, Spud Roselli, or your right-hander, Karl Jurgenson?

—To bring in Jurgenson, turn to page 42.

—To bring in Roselli, turn to page 38.

You flash the bunt sign. Lou picks it up and responds with a nod. Your third-base coach relays the sign to Skeets at first.

Lou squares, lays down a nice sacrifice bunt. With Skeets on second and two out, Moose Harrington lumbers up to bat. He stares out at the mound. He takes a few pitches. Ball one. Strike one. Then—crunch—Moose wallops a line drive into left field.

(continued on page 35)

Skeets comes tearing around third, heading home. The play will be close. You cross your fingers. Skeets slides. The umpire signals.

He is safe! You win 5–4 with some good, solid managing. You run onto the field. Everyone is dancing around home plate. Fans and players are giving each other high fives. Your players form a big circle and hoist you and Skeets up in the air for a victory ride into the locker room.

The End

Edwards has hit well against Tobler in the past. So you put the second-string catcher up to hit.

Overeager, Edwards swings at the first pitch. He grounds it right back to the mound and the pitcher fires to second. But no one is covering. Tony Mason slipped coming over. The ball rolls into center field. Lopez races to third and holds there. Jet Johnson singles off a shaken-up Tobler, and Lopez comes home with the winning run.

You win the World Series. With a little help from a stumbling shortstop.

The End

Roscoe's first pitch to Percy is drilled into center for a run-scoring base hit. That puts the Terriers ahead 5–4, a lead they hold to win the World Series.

You cannot believe how stupid you were. If you had walked Percy, you would have set up a double-play situation and been able to pitch to a less dangerous hitter. You want to take a long, long shower. You hope that, maybe if you stay in the shower long enough, you will melt and dissolve down the drain.

The End

In his first two Series appearances, Roselli just couldn't get the Terriers out. And he can't today. Roselli lets up five runs before you put Jurgenson into the game. Jurgy has pretty good stuff and holds the Terriers through the top of the ninth.

You are ahead 6–5, but the Terriers are threatening. Their catcher, Quintero Pinson, singles. Hank Percy pops out, but Brad Boysenberry triples, and Pinson scores the tying run. Terrier manager Arthur London removes Boysenberry for a pinch runner, Gnat Arnold. Gnat is not much of a baseball player, but he is incredibly fast—used to be a track star at Arizona State—and London uses him in pinch-run and steal situations.

Another reason you want to win the World Series is a private one. It has to do with the Terriers' manager. You owe a lot to Arthur London, the Grand Old Man of Baseball. He was your manager when you were a young second baseman just starting out in the majors; he brought you up from the minor

(continued on page 39)

leagues when no one else would give you a chance. You still remember him putting his arm around you and saying, in a fatherly way, "You're smart. You can play in the Bigs." When your career ended, London made you his third-base coach. He taught you almost everything you know about baseball. Today, however, you desperately want to beat him.

You think you know London's mind. Especially in this situation. One out, tie score, top of the ninth, good runner on third, good bunter at the plate. The situation is tailor-made for a suicide squeeze, with the runner racing toward home and the batter knocking the ball on the ground.

The only way to beat a squeeze is by throwing the ball at the batter's head. He has to duck and cannot make contact. The catcher tags out the runner who is on his way home.

If you think you know Arthur London's mind well enough to predict a squeeze, you will call for a high, inside fastball. If you are not sure, you will let Jurgy pitch his regular way.

—To predict the squeeze, turn to page 43.

—To let Jurgy pitch his regular way, turn to page 50.

"Jet," you say to your second baseman. "Listen. Just go up there and get me a fly ball. Any field. Just get it up in the air."

Jet goes up to the plate. He looks uncomfortable. His hands are way down at the end of the bat, and he is holding his arms lower than usual so he can get under the ball. The pitch is a letter-high fastball—the type of pitch Jet usually ropes for extra bases. Not now. He pops the ball up, and the Terriers' catcher makes the play.

You overmanaged. You should never change a player's natural swing in the middle of a game. When Skeets grounds out and then the Terriers score three runs in the tenth to beat you, you have no one to blame but yourself.

The End

Good move. You walk Percy, and Boysenberry hits a ground ball to shortstop. Slick Desmond turns it into an inning-ending double play.

In the bottom of the ninth, it is still a tie ball game. The Jet strikes out. Skeets draws a walk, and Lou strides up to the plate. Lou has been steaming hot all Series. He has two hits already today and lined out his third time up.

Still, this situation calls for a bunt. All the percentages say that you should have Lou bunt and move Skeets into scoring position.

—*If you want Lou to bunt, turn to page 34.*

—*If you want Lou to swing away, turn to page 28.*

You have never believed in the statistics that show left-handed hitters do better against right-handed pitchers. Your strategy has always been to go with individuals, not numbers. Today, you are going to go with Jurgenson, your righty.

The Terriers rock Jurgenson for five runs. Then they get three more off your short-relief man, right-hander Richard Roscoe. The last time you saw such fireworks was the Fourth of July.

The Terriers are champs. You are going home a loser. But a believer—in percentages.

The End

You have spent more time sitting around talking baseball with Art London than many men have spent talking to their wives. You and he think alike.

You signal your catcher, Bruce Marshall, to call—one time—for a fastball high and tight. Jurgy winds and throws inside to the batter.

Gnat Arnold is not coming. He is standing right at third. The squeeze was not on. Your pitcher wasted a pitch, and you are *confused*. On the next pitch, you realize what London is up to. He has waited until now to call the squeeze. Here comes Gnat. There goes the bunt. Jurgy charges, scoops, flips to Marshall. Gnat slides—and scores what turns out to be the winning run.

You tried to outsmart Arthur London. But you forgot the first lesson he ever taught you. "Son," he had said long ago, "never try to predict what someone else is thinking. Always expect the unexpected." That is why he—not you—is the best manager in baseball.

The End

You have not used Terrence Brown all Series. He is getting old, and his bat is not as quick as it used to be. You have been saving him for a special moment; a moment when the pressure is so great almost anyone else would choke. Under that kind of pressure—at this moment—there is no one in the world you'd rather have at bat than the veteran, Old Reliable Terrence Brown.

"Terrence. You are up there," you yell. He gets up from the bench and walks to the bat rack. He pulls down his famous black bat. Fans call Terrence "Reliable Terrence Brown." And they call his bat "The Old Reliable Stick."

You say what you always say when you want him to bat: "Terrence, you got a hit for me?" Terrence smiles and says what he always says: "Not for you, Skipper. I got one for the whole team and for all the good ball fans in America."

Relaxed, cool, Terrence never gets rattled. He walks up to the plate as if he is heading out for a Sunday picnic.

(continued on page 46)

Patiently, Terrence takes the first pitch for a strike. He is just sizing up the pitcher. Terrence has never hit against Tobler before. When Terrence first started playing pro ball, the best players were paid $60,000, maybe $75,000, a year. Terrence has never made more than $80,000 a season. He looks out at the Terriers' six-million-dollar pitcher and waggles his Old Reliable Stick into his comfortable stance.

Tobler fires. Terrence swings. Base hit, opposite field. Terrence jogs to first. Lopez holds at second. The fans give Terrence a standing ovation.

Jet Johnson is the batter with one out in the bottom of the ninth and the winning run on second base. First pitch, Lopez steals third.

All you need is a fly ball to win the World Series. Do you tell Jet to try to hit a fly ball or let him go up to the plate and swing naturally?

—To tell Jet to hit a fly ball, turn to page 40.

—To let him swing naturally, turn to page 48.

You walk over to the bat rack. Moose Harrington is going up to bat. "Moose," you yell. "Let me rub some hits into that bat."

Moose gives you the bat. You rub it. Maybe you can put some hits in the bat. You don't know. You are feeling helpless.

When Moose strikes out on three pitches, you cannot think straight. You pick up a bat and bang it against the wall of the dugout. The bat splinters into pieces.

You lose 5–0. You are still upset, but smashing up the bat took away some of the frustration.

The End

You realize there is enough pressure already. Jet has enough to think about in this situation. He is thinking: watch the ball; make contact in front of the plate; drive in the run. Jet Johnson is a seasoned pro. He knows what has to be done. Best not to offer any advice; just a little encouragement.

"Knock 'em in, Jet. You can do it," you say from the bench.

That is all it takes. The pitch from Tobler is a letter-high fastball. The kind Jet loves to rip. He jumps all over the ball, roping it into right field. As soon as the ball hits the ground, Lopez scampers home with the winning run.

You win the World Series 2–1.

Fans are going crazy in the stands. The guys with antler horns, members of the Moose Harrington Fan Club, are dancing for joy in left field. CAT-MAN is clawing and gnashing his heart out on top of the Bomber dugout.

(continued on page 49)

You run into the locker room. Victory. Everyone is going nuts.

Everyone except Terrence Brown. Terrence stands up on the bench in front of the row of lockers. All eyes focus on the Old Reliable veteran.

"Folks, I have been in this game a long time. There's nothing I love more than baseball," he says slowly and with emotion. "Baseball's kind fans and all the teammates and coaches I've ever played with have been good to Ol' Terrence. I've been waiting a long time to play in the World Series. And it is great to win one. It is great to win the Series for all the great Bomber fans and all the good ball fans in America. Winning the World Series was my last dream for baseball. Having won it today, I feel fulfilled at this time as I announce my retirement."

There are tears running from everyone's eyes. Baseball just will not be the same without Terrence Brown around. But what a way to retire—as World Series champion!

The End

You think about guessing "squeeze," but remember one of the first lessons Art London ever taught you. He told you never to try to predict what someone else is thinking. "Always expect the unexpected," he said. It would be logical to call a squeeze now. Too logical.

Jurgy winds, fires, and the batter takes strike one down the middle. There was no squeeze. Hmm. You wonder what London is up to, but you dare not try to predict it. Second pitch. Fastball, letter high. Here it is—the squeeze is on! The batter squares and fouls off the high fastball. With two strikes on a batter, it is too much of a risk to try a bunt. You have taken away the Terriers' squeeze-play option. Soon, they go down without scoring.

In the bottom of the ninth, Billy Sawatski doubles and steals third. With one out, Slick Desmond hits a pop-up foul behind third base. As soon as the Terrier third baseman turns his back to the plate and makes the catch, Coach Peters yells: "Tag." Sawatski races home and beats a late throw with the winning run.

(continued on page 51)

You outsmarted Art London without trying to outsmart him. Your intelligent managing beat the best. In the locker room, after the game, the phone rings. It is Art London calling from the Terriers' clubhouse. "Pal," he says. "If I had to lose, it couldn't have been to a better person."

You have never been so proud in your life.

The End

Percy is too dangerous. He is too good a hitter to play games with. If you shift, he will go the other way or drop a bunt down the third-base line. He has a big ego, but he also has a lot of talent. The only way to get Percy out is by throwing pitches he can't hit.

Roselli has good stuff tonight. His fastball is deceptively quick and his curve is breaking down. He is a gutsy little left-hander and should give Percy trouble.

The crowd is silent as Percy strolls to the plate. There is a staring match going on between batter and pitcher. Roselli checks the sign from his catcher. He throws the pitch. A fastball. Quick—but not too quick for Percy to get around on. Percy takes a big cut and stings a two-hop ground ball toward the bag at first. Lou Robinson reaches across his body toward the foul line, snatches the ball out of right field, and taps the bag with his foot.

(continued on page 53)

What a great play. Since you moved him to first from the outfield, Lou has really been improving as an infielder. That was a great play, with real infielder instincts.

Rex Tobler is pitching well for the Terriers, and the game goes scoreless into the fourth inning.

In the bottom of the fourth, Slick Desmond singles with no one out. Eddie Cooper is the batter. Cooper has to move Slick into scoring position. The best way to do it would be with a bunt. But the Terriers will be expecting a bunt. Their first baseman and third baseman will be charging in. It might pay off if Cooper fakes a bunt, pulls his bat back, and slashes the ball past the charging infielders.

—*If you want Cooper to bunt, turn to page 60.*

—*If you want him to try a slash, turn to page 56.*

Nothing else has stopped Hank Percy. Maybe a shift will.

Your catcher, Bruce Marshall, gives Roselli an inside target. This will make it more difficult for Percy to go the opposite way with the ball. And that is exactly what he is trying to do. Percy's feet are shifted into a closed stance, with his front foot six inches in front of his back foot. The big lefty will try to punch the ball into left field for an easy base hit.

But Percy is not used to slapping at the ball. He is used to rearing back and taking his big, powerful home-run swing. Now, he looks awkward. He swings at and misses an inside fastball. Strike one. He takes a pitch for strike two. Percy is way off balance. Zip. Strike three.

(continued on page 55)

Neither team scores for the first three innings. In the top of the fourth, Tony Mason leads off with a single for the Terriers. The Terriers' number two hitter is Quintero Pinson, their catcher.

With the game tied 0–0 and both pitchers looking strong, you think Pinson may try a sacrifice bunt intended to move Mason into scoring position. This seems to be shaping up into the type of game where one run might be all that is needed to win.

To defense the probable bunt, you are considering having your first and third basemen charge. There is not much anyone can do against a good bunt. But if the ball is bunted a little bit too hard, a charging infielder may have a play at second. If Pinson is not bunting, however, he could rap a ground ball by the charging infielders.

—*To have your infielders charge, turn to page 98.*

—*To have them stay back, turn to page 94.*

The Terriers' first and third basemen charge on the pitch. As Cooper drops his bat to waist level, the second baseman races over to cover first. Suddenly, Cooper pulls the bat back. He slashes at the pitch and knocks a ground ball into right field for a single. He hit it smack where the second baseman would have been if Cooper hadn't faked the bunt.

Desmond sprints toward third and slides in safely, beating the throw from right.

You are really fired up now. Nobody out. Time to start a rally. Time to paw, claw, and scratch out some runs.

(continued on page 57)

Cooper steals second. Marshall singles in two runs. Roselli strikes out, and then Jet Johnson and Skeets Rodriguez hit back-to-back doubles to put the Clawing Cats ahead 4–0.

Leroy Marlin comes in to pitch for the Terriers. He does not make as much money as Rex Tobler, but is very good. Marlin is a right-hander with a tricky screwball.

He gets the side out in the fourth inning.

(continued on page 58)

The Terriers score twice in the fifth inning and once in the sixth. Meanwhile, Marlin does not allow a hit.

You are still ahead 4–3 in the top of the seventh, but the Terriers are threatening. With two out, Tony Mason doubles. The tying run is on second base as catcher Quintero Pinson steps up.

Pinson is a good clutch hitter. This is just the type of situation he likes to be in. He is patient. He is a fastball hitter and a master of working the count and waiting for his pitch.

He works the count to 3–2. Roselli has to come in with a strike, or he puts the go-ahead run on base. Roselli's best pitch is a fastball, but he might be able to sneak a curve past Pinson for strike three.

Bruce Marshall, your catcher, glances over to the dugout. You flash him the sign for the type of pitch you want Roselli to throw.

—*To have Roselli fire a fastball, turn to page 87.*

—*To have him twist off a curve, turn to page 64.*

The runner on second cannot believe no one is holding him on. He looks around. The second baseman is playing back. The shortstop is playing back. He looks into center field. Nope. The center fielder is not sneaking up from behind.

He looks over to his third-base coach. The Terriers' third-base coach nods and goes through a set of signals. Roscoe releases the pitch. The man on second takes off for third. Marshall's throw is low and skips into left field. The runner scores. The man on first goes to second. On the next pitch, Mark Wright bangs a base hit into right field and the runner from second scores, putting the Terriers ahead 2–1.

That is all the scoring for the rest of the game. You gave the Terriers an opportunity. They took it and won the World Series.

The End

Cooper lays down a nice bunt. As you suspected, the Terriers' first and third basemen were charging. The bunt is good, but the Terrier third baseman comes flying in and scoops up the ball with one hand. He pivots and fires to second to try to force out Desmond.

Desmond slides. The throw is not in time. But— oh, no!—Desmond overslides the base. Tony Mason, the Terrier shortstop, tags Slick out.

Stupid base-running. You can understand and forgive your players for making physical errors or missing practice for good reasons. But there is nothing you hate more than sloppy mental mistakes. You don't even want to talk to Desmond when he comes back to the dugout. But you know that he is the type of player who will brood like a baby if you don't give him encouragement.

(continued on page 61)

"It's all right, Slick. You'll get them next time," you say to your stupid shortstop.

Cooper steals second on the next pitch. He slides in properly and stays on the bag after the throw. Bruce Marshall, your catcher, singles Cooper home. You go ahead 1–0 after four full innings of play.

The Terriers battle back and put a runner in scoring position in the top of the seventh inning. It looks like your pitcher, Roselli, might be in trouble. He is throwing a bit high, a sign of tiredness. When a pitcher starts throwing high late in games, that means trouble. It often means that he will hang a curve ball or groove a letter-high fastball. And if that happens, it often means GOODBYE! Goodbye, first, to the ball when it is socked for a home run. Goodbye, second, to the pitcher who gets taken out of the game and sent to the showers.

You walk out to the mound.

(continued on page 62)

"How's the arm feel, Spud?" you ask the pitcher.

"Loose, Coach. Loose and easy," he replies.

You've been out to a lot of mound meetings before, and you know that when a pitcher is really feeling good, he says his arm is "Great!" with a lot of enthusiasm. A pitcher hardly ever admits to being tired. If he is tired, he will say something like what Roselli just said.

You look at Marshall and the catcher shakes his head. "The ball isn't popping, not like the early innings," Marshall says.

That makes your decision easy. Time to bring in Richard Roscoe. Roscoe is a good short-relief man with a blazing fastball.

(continued on page 63)

There is one out and the Terriers have runners on first and second. While you are out on the mound, waiting for Roscoe to come in from the bull pen, you wave your shortstop and second baseman into the meeting.

You have a defensive decision to make. Coming to bat for the Terriers is Mark Wright, their left fielder. Wright bats right-handed and hits well to all fields. He has good bat control and gets most of his hits on ground balls and low line drives through the infield.

In this situation, you have to decide if you want your shortstop and second baseman to stay back and try to turn one of Wright's ground balls into a double play or if they should keep the runner on second close to the bag. The runner is pretty fast, and, unless you decoy and keep him close, he will be able to score on a single.

—To have your shortstop and second baseman decoy the runner, turn to page 72.

—To have them play back, turn to page 59.

Pinson is thinking fastball. No chance. You would rather walk him with a wild curve than give him his pitch while he is waiting for it. You touch your cap, flashing Marshall the bench-to-catcher signal for the curve. Then you walk to the spot near the water cooler where you stand during most of the game, especially in tense situations.

"Snap it off, Spud. Break it down good," you mutter to yourself, urging your pitcher on.

Roselli nods at Marshall's sign. The pitcher kicks and throws a curve. Pinson starts his swing, but the ball disappears down by his toes. Strike three! Oh, was he fooled. That ends the inning. And it saves you two runs, because Percy leads off the Terriers' eighth with a game-tying home run. If Percy had hit that blast with Mason and Pinson on base last inning, you would be playing come-from-behind baseball.

(continued on page 66)

As it stands, in the bottom of the eighth, the score is tied. With two out, Eddie Cooper is on third. The scheduled hitter is Roselli, your pitcher.

You have a whole row of hitters better than Roselli. It might be a good time for a pinch hitter. But besides that home-run ball he threw to Percy, Roselli has been pitching fairly well. Sure, he has been in trouble a few times, but he has pitched his way out.

(continued on page 67)

You look down the bench from your spot near the water cooler. There are three or four guys who could go up there and be a threat with the bat. Lawrence Silver would be your man if you decide to go with a pinch hitter. He is a right-handed hitter and should not have much trouble with Leroy Marlin's screwball. If you pinch-hit for Roselli, you still have Jerry Crane in the bull pen. Crane could come in and pitch the ninth—and possibly extra innings if the score stays tied. Roselli has thrown eight good innings. He probably wants to stay in the game.

But you are the manager. The decision is yours.

—If you decide to keep Roselli in the game, turn to page 68.

—To take him out for a pinch hitter, turn to page 76.

Your mind works quickly. You never spend too much time pondering tough decisions. They have to be made fast, or you go back over them in your head, second- and third-guessing yourself. The pace of this game is going well. Pinch hitters are never foolproof.

There will be no change. With the score tied in the bottom of the eighth, Roselli will bat for himself. Maybe he will get a hit. Maybe not. But he is going to get a chance to win his own ball game, and he is going to go back out there to pitch in the ninth.

When Leroy Marlin, the Terriers' pitcher, sees Roselli coming out to hit, he can't believe it. Marlin turns around and checks the scoreboard—sure enough, there are two outs. That means a squeeze bunt would be ineffective. Roselli needs a base hit to knock in Cooper.

(continued on page 69)

The fans start a rhythmic clap. The scoreboard flashes "Claw!" Marlin fires a fastball—strike one. He fires a wicked screwball—strike two. He throws a fastball low and way outside. The ball scoots by the catcher and rolls to the backstop. Cooper tears in from third. The catcher picks up the ball and throws to Marlin covering home. Cooper slides. The umpire calls him safe.

Roselli strikes out on the next pitch. But it doesn't matter. You are ahead 5–4 going into the ninth inning.

(continued on page 70)

Pinch hitter Pete Epsy leads off the Terrier ninth. He slaps Roselli's first pitch into left field for a single. Reggie Trowbridge is the next Terrier batter. With no one out and the tying run on first base, everybody in the stadium knows what Trowbridge is going to do. Your third baseman plays in close, expecting a bunt. At first, Lou Robinson holds Epsy close and then charges on the pitch.

Trowbridge spins a good bunt down the first-base line. Your catcher, Bruce Marshall, bounds out from behind the plate and pounces on the ball. Without hesitation, he fires toward second base, where Slick Desmond has come over to get the throw. But Slick could not get this one if he were seven feet tall. The ball sails into center field, and Epsy races to third.

(continued on page 71)

Ouch. That hurts. Your clutch catcher making a mistake like that. A rookie mistake. Overeager, releasing the ball too early. The Terriers put Gnat Arnold, their superspeedster, in to run for Trowbridge. This will put even more pressure on Marshall. Gnat is always a threat to steal.

There he goes. Gnat is stealing on the first pitch. Marshall pops up even quicker than last time. He snaps off a quick throw toward second. Right on the money. Slick raps on the tag. Then Billy Sawatski yells from third: "HOME! He's going!" As soon as Marshall released the ball, Epsy took off for home. Quite a gamble. Desmond spins around and aims the ball toward Marshall at the plate.

It is the bunt throw in reverse, sailing high over Marshall's head. Epsy scores the tying run.

The score remains tied until the eleventh inning. In the eleventh, the Terriers win on Hank Percy's home run. The Bombers had the World Series in their grasp. This was one they really let slip away.

The End

"Got to keep the runner close at second," you tell your infielders. When Desmond and Jet Johnson decoy a runner, it is like watching a set of windshield wipers. Desmond hustles in behind the runner from shortstop; then as soon as Slick backs out, Jet is there to keep the runner close.

Roscoe finishes his warm-up tosses and everybody is set at his position. Slick and Jet keep the runner close at second. Roscoe fires his heat. Wright swings and misses on the first two pitches. On the 0–2 pitch, Wright barely gets his bat on the ball. Just enough to tap a looping line drive for a hit to right field.

The runner from second momentarily thinks about trying to score. But a powerful throw from Skeets Rodriguez changes that idea quickly. The runner stops at third. Good thing you had your infielders keep him close.

(continued on page 73)

Bases loaded. One out. This is a tough spot for Roscoe. But he likes tough situations. His fastball seems to get faster and his control more precise. Roscoe really bears down and concentrates when the pressure is on. He throws his fastball so hard that sometimes his hat falls off.

He stares in at the Terrier batter. The pitch—a blazing heater—is tapped back to the mound. Roscoe loses his hat but finds the ball. He fires home to Marshall, who touches the plate and then shoots the ball down to Lou Robinson at first. Double play.

(continued on page 74)

You are still winning 1–0 in the bottom of the eighth inning. Some of your players are starting to get outwardly excited. It is as if the excitement from the fans in the stands has seeped its way into the dugout. There are a lot of smiles on the bench. Players are urging each other on. You can hear the dancing footsteps of CATMAN as he leads cheers from atop the Bombers' dugout.

The excitement is spreading to you as well. You look down at your finger and can imagine that World Series championship ring. You can see it glittering and shining. Immediately, you slap yourself in the face. Got to wake up. It is still the eighth inning. It is nice to daydream, but there will be plenty of time for dreaming later. Now is a time for managing.

"Couple of runs, guys," you yell. "We need some insurance runs."

(continued on page 75)

You don't get any runs and the Terriers come to bat only one run down in the top of the ninth.

Leading off is Tony Mason. He is scrappy and good. He has been the best shortstop in baseball for years. He goes up to bat fighting. He attacks the first pitch and drills a single into center field. Terrier catcher Quintero Pinson makes a sacrifice bunt which moves Mason into scoring position.

Desmond and Jet keep Mason close. Roscoe strikes out home-run hitter Hank Percy for the second out of the inning. Burly Brad Boysenberry, the Terriers' cleanup man, steps up to the plate.

Desmond and Jet have been doing a pretty good job at getting in behind Mason as decoys at second. You do not particularly want to have to pitch to Boysenberry. It might be a good idea to try to pick Mason off.

—To put on a pickoff play, turn to page 84.

—To pitch to Boysenberry, turn to page 102.

There are three things you have found a manager has to do in these high-pressure, game-on-the-line situations. First, he has to make a decision. Second, he has to stick with it. Last, he has to pray.

As Silver walks up to the plate, all you can do is observe the last of your three managerial commandments. You say a quick prayer as Silver digs in to face Leroy Marlin.

Marlin checks Cooper at third. He stares in at Silver and fires a fastball low and away for a ball. The Terriers' catcher makes a nice defensive effort to save a wild pitch. Next pitch is low for ball two. Silver fouls off a pitch and the fourth pitch is inside for a ball. With a three-and-one count, Marlin might come in with a juicy pitch. If not, you would love to see Silver draw a walk and get Jet Johnson up to bat.

(continued on page 77)

The pitch is outside for ball four. Silver trots down to first. You put your fast utility infielder, Walter Lopez, in as a pinch runner for Silver. You are not going to try any fancy steals—not with two outs. But it never hurts to have some extra speed on the base paths. Maybe Lopez will be able to keep the inning alive by beating out a force play at second or decoying in front of a ground ball to make for a tough play on an otherwise easy pickup.

(continued on page 78)

Little decisions like this one often make a difference in the last innings of a close ball game. Your club might not have all the big bats and highly paid superstars of the Terriers, but you hope that your intelligent managing can make up for some of the difference.

Jet Johnson is due up. He has been spectacular all season. He stole 70 bases and scored 100 runs. Last year, the Bombers' old manager did not even think the Jet was good enough to make the starting lineup. You fixed that. It took one small adjustment, and—like magic—Jet was the best second baseman in the league.

He always had a great glove. But the Bombers were not utilizing Jet's great speed on offense. Jet had always been a switch hitter. He was a switch hitter in college and in the minor leagues. That was how he hit his first few years in the pros.

(continued on page 79)

When you were hired to manage the Bombers, you looked at all your players' statistics. And when you were studying Jet's stats, you noticed that his batting average left-handed was 30 points higher than right-handed. You realized that the type of hitter Jet is—a slap-and-smack hitter who relies more on his speed than on his power—always does better from the left side of the plate. The left side is a step closer to first base. Hitting left-handed, Jet can bang balls into the artificial turf and beat out big hops for infield hits. From the right side of the plate, he loses that extra step.

(continued on page 80)

Jet was a little annoyed when you told him you wanted him to bat entirely from the left side. He said all his home runs last year came when he batted from the right side. You said you would trade his three home runs a year for an extra thirty points on his batting average, any day.

And that is exactly what happened. Jet's batting average shot up. But he still fools around batting right-handed in batting practice. He likes to show off his "power."

One day, before a game, Jet challenged Lou Robinson and Moose Harrington to a home-run-hitting contest in batting practice.

"In ten pitches," Jet said, "I bet you I can hit more home runs right-handed than you two can hit out of the infield batting from the opposite side of the plate."

Lou and Moose took Jet up on the bet. Whoever lost would have to be the winner's chauffeur for a while.

(continued on page 81)

Jet lost. But he never had to actually pay off, because he bet the pair double or nothing that he could beat them both in a running race—if he ran backward and they ran forward. Jet might not be much of a power hitter, but he runs like a bullet—even backward.

Now, in the eighth inning of the final game of the World Series, runners on first and third, two out and a tie score, Jet is ready to go to bat. First, he comes over to talk to you.

He says that because Marlin has such a good screwball, he wants to hit right-handed instead of left-handed. Marlin is a right-handed pitcher, but his wicked screwball is tough for left-handed hitters to hit.

Jet has a point. If he bats righty, he takes away Marlin's greatest strength—his screwball. But Jet also sacrifices his greatest asset—his speed from the left side of the plate.

—*If you let Jet bat right-handed, turn to page 88.*

—*If you make him hit left-handed, turn to page 90.*

During spring training, Lou Robinson had been as
eager as a rookie. He was being switched from the
outfield to first base, and he had a lot to learn. Day
after day, Lou remained on the field long after the
regular eight hours' practice. On one of those days,
you, he, and Slick Desmond were practicing rundowns. The Bombers' batboy, a local kid, was running between first and second. Lou and Desmond
would throw the ball back and forth, trying to trap
the batboy in less than three throws.

Every four or five rundowns, you would yell
"HOME!" and whoever had the ball would pivot
and fire to you at the plate. It was just a drill, but
you never can tell when that skill might prove useful
in a game situation.

(continued on page 83)

This is it. This is the situation you, Lou, Slick, and the batboy had practiced for in spring training.

Mason is steaming toward the plate. Bomber catcher Bruce Marshall screams: "HOME!" Lou has won hundreds of games with his bat. Can he win one with his arm?

Lou hears Marshall yell, pivots, and fires to the plate. Mason slides. Marshall falls on top of the runner in a mist of dust and a tangle of flying arms and legs.

The throw is perfect. The tag is there. The runner is out.

You hold on to win 4–3. World Series champions.

Tomorrow, all the papers will write about Lou Robinson's great plays—this throw and the backhand scoop in the first inning. You know about those extra hours of hard work in spring training. You know about the long hours of dirty sweat in tiring heat which made his great plays—and your World Series ring—possible.

The End

Jet is the quicker of the two. He and Desmond work the pickoff at second base like a finely tuned Swiss clock. They click. For the last few decoys, they have gotten Mason accustomed to a rhythm. Desmond comes in behind him, then backs off. When Desmond backs off, Mason takes a couple of steps toward third. The Jet comes in from second and Mason moves back toward the bag.

On the live pickoff, Slick and Jet change the rhythm a half beat. As soon as Slick begins moving out, the Jet flies in. This catches the runner off guard, and, if the pitcher has good timing, the play usually works.

It is a timing play.

It has worked in tough situations all year. You just hope it can work now. You start off the play by taking off your cap and scratching your head. That tells Marshall it is going to be a pickoff with the second baseman covering.

(continued on page 85)

Marshall relays the signal. Jet acknowledges it by putting his glove hand on his knee. Roscoe comes into his stretch. A count begins as soon as Desmond starts for the bag. One. Two. Three. Jet takes off. Four. Roscoe pivots and fires at the base. Jet arrives at the base at the same time as the ball.

And a split second before Mason.

Mason dives head first back to second. Jet touches the runner on the arm. "Out!" yells the umpire.

(continued on page 86)

What a great way to end it. Winning on a pickoff play. The Clawing Cats, the team that nobody thought would go anywhere, have pawed their way to the baseball championship of the world.

Now you can start dreaming. You have won the division title, won the pennant, won the World Series, and will surely be named Manager of the Year. There is no more baseball managing to be done until spring training. Now come the victory celebrations, the ticker-tape parade, the advertising endorsements, speaking engagements. Now comes the thrill of being recognized and asked for your autograph at restaurants all over the country.

Wow! What a little guts and good timing can do for you.

The End

Marshall nods as he picks up your sign. It is going to be a fastball. But Pinson drives the pitch into center field for a hit.

A good throw by a charging Eddie Cooper holds Mason at third.

Hank Percy, the Terriers' right fielder, steps up to the plate. First pitch, he takes low and outside. Marshall looks down to first, fires to Lou Robinson, and they have Pinson trapped in a rundown.

Lou tosses to shortstop Slick Desmond. Pinson turns and heads back to first. Desmond flips back to Lou. All of a sudden, Mason takes off from third. He is heading for home. Out of the corner of his eye, Lou sees Mason going.

It is the top of the seventh and Mason will be the tying run if he scores.

In spring training, when you were teaching Lou how to play first base, you went over this exact situation. What did you teach him? To get the sure out in the rundown? Or to cut off the runner going home?

—If you taught Lou to get the sure out, turn to page 89.

—If you taught him to try to cut off the runner going home, turn to page 82.

If Jet is that nervous about Marlin's screwball, why not give him a shot from the right side? It will sure surprise Marlin when Jet comes up batting right-handed. And it may shock him into a wild pitch or a sloppy mistake—like a pitch right down the pipe.

Jet takes a few practice swings from the right side. He looks pretty good. Marlin looks pretty confused.

The first pitch is a fastball. Jet hits it. A long fly ball. Right to the Terriers' left fielder. A little more power and that ball might have been a home run. But you didn't need a home run; all you needed was a single.

Jet's fly ball ends the inning, and the Terriers get a run off Crane in the top of the ninth. That is all they need to beat you 5–4.

The End

Lou came down to spring training eager and excited. He was about to learn a new position, and you were the one who would teach the old outfielder how to play first base.

Your goal in bringing Lou around as a first baseman was to make him adequate. If he could hold down the job at first without hurting the team in the field, you figured his bat would more than make up for his average defensive play. So, when you worked on the rundown drills, you stressed getting the runner out and not worrying about what else was occurring.

Right now, as Mason races toward the plate, those old lessons seem to have stuck. Lou is letting the runner score. He is going for the sure out.

But no out is a sure out. Lou flips back to Desmond and the ball pops out of Desmond's glove. Mason scores. Pinson dives safely into second and scores on a single by Percy. The Terriers hold you scoreless for the rest of the game. The Bombers lose 5–4.

Next year, you will have extra practice on how to execute a rundown. But practice next March is not going to help you face defeat today.

The End

"Jet," you say, "are you nuts? Remember what happened the last time you seriously tried to hit from the right side? You nearly spent two weeks as a chauffeur. Get up there left-handed and if he throws you that stupid screwball, drill it."

"Right," Jet responds. "Drill the screwball."

Not many people have called Leroy Marlin's screwball "stupid." It is one of the best pitches in the major leagues. But you strictly believe that if Jet goes up there with enough confidence, he can drill that screwball as if it were a Little Leaguer's lollipop pitch.

(continued on page 91)

Jet steps into the batter's box—the left-hander's batter's box. He settles in, convinced that he will keep his head and shoulder locked in and get a hit.

Marlin's first pitch is inside. Jet hangs tough. It is a fastball, though, and is not breaking. At the last moment, Jet drops his bat and ducks out the way.

The fans boo. They think Marlin is throwing at Jet. He is, in a way. But it is good, hard baseball. Marlin threw a brushback pitch trying to scare Jet into being timid up at bat.

"C'mon, Jet," you yell.

(continued on page 93)

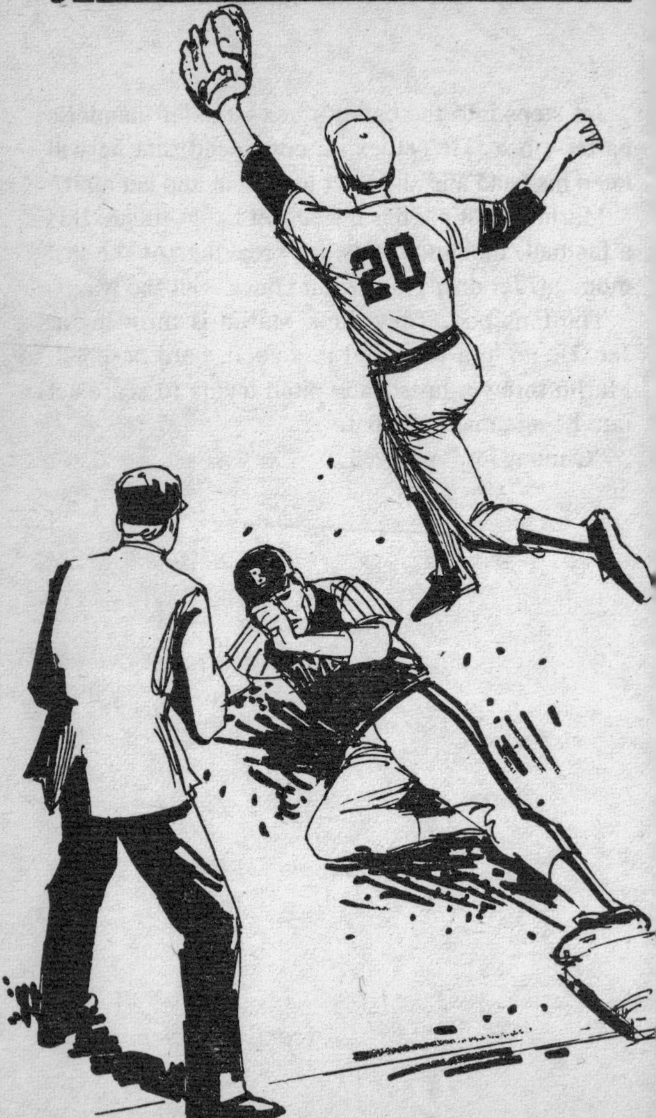
20

Marlin delivers his second pitch. This time it is a screwball. It breaks over the plate. Jet swings, makes contact, and sends the ball flying toward the gap in left-center field. The ball hits the ground, gets by the Terrier center fielder, and rolls to the foot of the fence 380 feet away from home plate.

Cooper scores. Lopez scores. Jet slides into third with a triple.

What a clutch hit. The fans are going crazy. Everyone is going crazy. Players are jumping up and down in the dugout. Veterans like Lou Robinson and rookies like Kid Costello are dancing and giving each other high fives.

Skeets Rodriguez strikes out to end the inning, but Jerry Crane holds the Terriers scoreless in the top of the ninth and you win 6–4.

In the locker room after the game, you overhear Jet jabbering away with Lou and Moose. "That was nothing," Jet is saying. "If I'd been up there batting righty, that ball would have been gone."

The game-winning triple was good enough, as far as you are concerned.

The End

With the score tied, you decide to play it safe. Infield back, everyone alert, reacting to what happens, not trying to predict what will occur.

When Pinson squares to bunt the first pitch, you slap yourself. When he drops the ball down the third-base line and beats it out for a single, you slap yourself harder.

All season, you have been taking chances. All season, those chances have been paying off. That is the way you got into the World Series—aggressive, hard, attacking Clawball-style baseball. That is the brand of baseball the Clawing Cats are known for. There is an old sports saying which goes like this: "I'm gonna dance with the girl I brought to the prom." Well, you got to the World Series playing Clawball. Now, you have begun to pussyfoot it.

(continued on page 95)

Your timid action results in the Terriers having runners on first and second with no outs in the fourth inning. Hank Percy is the batter. He pulls a Roselli fastball deep, deep to right field. CATMAN leaps up and does body language trying to hex the ball and make it curve foul. No such luck. The ball stays fair for a home run. You can shift all you want, but the best shift in baseball cannot stop a home run.

The game remains 3–0 into the sixth inning.

(continued on page 96)

You are fed up with everyone's lackadaisical play. And you are sick and tired of your lazy managing. You did not come all the way to Game Seven of the World Series to sit back and watch your championship chances self-destruct in front of your eyes.

In the top of the sixth, Jet Johnson and Slick Desmond both make errors. The Terriers score two more runs. They are ahead 5–0. And there is no sign that the momentum is about to change.

(continued on page 97)

You make pitching, fielding, hitting substitutions. You try a pep talk. You try arguing with the umpire. You try yelling at your players. You try giving them encouragement.

But nothing changes into the bottom of the ninth inning.

You turn to your players one last time.

"We're the Clawing Cats," you say. "Cats have nine lives. We've used eight of them. Let's make the best out of our ninth."

Nobody on the bench says a word.

Most of the time, you stand by the water cooler. Now, you are thinking of walking over to the bat-rack side of the dugout instead. Maybe a change of location will shift the trend of dismal stagnation on the field.

—If you walk to the bat-rack side of the dugout, turn to page 47.

—If you stay by the water cooler, turn to page 111.

Charge! You charged into the season. You charged through the play-offs. And you are going to charge in the final game of the World Series. You may not win, but you will not lose without a fight.

Billy Sawatski inches forward at third base. Lou Robinson kicks dirt behind him at first. Roselli goes into his windup, and the two men tear in from both sides of the infield.

Pinson bunts down the third-base line. Sawatski picks the ball up bare-handed. In one flowing movement, he wheels and fires a perfect throw to Slick Desmond crossing the bag at second. Slick fires to Jet Johnson, covering first, to complete the double play.

(continued on page 99)

"Charge!" flashes the electric scoreboard. The fans respond to the daring defensive play with a chorus of applause and cheering. They begin to chant "Claw, Cats, Claw! Claw, Cats, Claw!"

Excitement is spreading on the bench. All the players are slapping hands and clapping in rhythm with the chants coming from the stands.

Two of your reserve outfielders, Jamie Cross and Kid Costello, jump up on the bench and sing the song they sing whenever they get excited. A fan wrote the lyrics and sent them to a local newspaper which printed them in the sports section.

At the top of their lungs, Costello and Cross sing horribly out of tune:

"At bat, we hit off the best;
On defense, we get out the rest.

"We're number one on the field;
To no one do we yield.

"Any team at all we'll match,
'Cause we're the Cats who claw and scratch."

(continued on page 100)

You hate the song, but the players love it. It gets them excited on the bench. All except Terrence Brown. Terrence is your old veteran pinch hitter. Terrence never gets excited. He is so cool, it is said he doesn't even sweat during a heat wave.

After the song, Terrence shakes his head. "Baseball," he says, "ain't what it used to be." But beneath that cool and relaxed demeanor, you know that even Terrence Brown is getting excited. Hey, this is the World Series.

Roselli gets the third out, and in the bottom of the seventh inning, you get a run on a double by Eddie Cooper, followed by a Bruce Marshall single. Marshall is on first with two outs and the pitcher at bat. You want Roselli to pitch one more inning; then you are going to the bull pen. So it does not matter if Marshall gets thrown out attempting to steal second base. If that happens, you will be able to put up a pinch hitter to lead off the bottom of the eighth. You give Marshall the sign to steal second.

(continued on page 101)

Marshall is off with the pitch. The Terriers' catcher throws down to second. Tony Mason, covering on the play, tags Marshall good and hard right on Marshall's left hand.

Marshall is safe. But that left hand is the one he hurt before the play-offs. You can tell by the expression on Marshall's face that the tag caused him quite a bit of pain.

You and the trainer run onto the field. The trainer takes out a can of cold spray.

You want to keep Marshall in the game. He is your team leader. He is the man who has come through in the clutch all year. But with an injured hand, he may hurt the team more than help it. Your backup catcher, Albert Edwards, is a solid substitute. Maybe you should take Marshall out of the game.

If you do decide to take him out, now would be the time to do it. He is not that fast a runner, and you could put in a faster man to pinch-run.

—*To take Marshall out, turn to page 108.*

—*To leave Marshall in the game, turn to page 104.*

A wild throw. A botched tag. A freak happening like the ball hitting the runner in the helmet.

Those are all possibilities which make pickoff attempts dangerous. The top of the ninth inning with one out between you and the World Series championship is no time to play risky games. Better to just let Roscoe keep his mind on the batter, bear down, and blow a few fastballs by Brad Boysenberry.

Good, hard, solid baseball is what you want to watch right now. You don't really want to watch it. You are so nervous, you would rather just close your eyes and listen to the crowd response to determine what is occurring on the field.

You close your eyes.

You think that this—right now—might be the most nervous you have ever been in your life.

"Three strikes away. Three strikes away. Three strikes away." You repeat this over and over.

(continued on page 103)

By the tenth time you have repeated it, you are only two strikes away from a World Series victory. Then Roscoe blazes another fastball by Boysenberry. "One strike away. One strike away."

Crack.

You never cringed at the sound of bat hitting ball before. But the solid crack is followed by a smack of ball hitting glove. And then by a screaming roar of joy from the stands.

You don't have to open your eyes. You know what happened. You know that the ball was caught for the third out and that the World Series is over.

The End

"Bruce," you ask him, "how's it feel?"

There are not many players you would trust to tell you the truth. But Marshall is smart, and he is a great competitor. He would not lie to you. He would not tell you he wanted to stay in the game if he thought it would hurt the team.

"It hurts. But I've played hurt before," he says.

You really need Bruce's mind and leadership in the game now. The team always seems to play with a little more confidence when he is behind the plate. He has guts. And right now, you believe those guts are enough to overcome his injury.

"Shoot an extra shot of cold spray on that hand," you tell the trainer. To Bruce, you say, "You'll get another shot of spray after you score."

He does not score because Roselli strikes out. But you give him another shot of spray before he puts on the catcher's gear.

(continued on page 105)

The top of the eighth turns into a tough inning. Roselli is in trouble. The Terriers have runners on first and second. There is only one out and you decide that you have seen enough of Roselli. Jerry Crane is still out there in the bull pen. He has been warming up on and off throughout the game. His arm may not be completely rested since he pitched in Game Five. But in a pressure-packed moment like this, his adrenaline should be enough to go on.

You walk slowly out to the mound with your head down. You do not want to talk to anyone. You do not want Roselli or Marshall to talk you out of making this pitching change. When you get to the pitcher's mound, you stick out your hand and Roselli gives you the ball without a sound.

The scoreboard flashes a message: "Get them dogs. Claw, Cats, Claw!"

When Crane arrives at the mound, you give him the ball. He reaches for the resin bag, and you stalk back to the dugout.

(continued on page 106)

Crane drops the resin bag. He kicks the rubber and looks in at Marshall for the sign.

He fires a low and outside fastball. The Terrier batter hits a low and hard ground ball between first and second base. It looks like a base hit. But Jet Johnson propels himself into the hole, scoops the ball up, spins, and throws to Desmond coming across second base. Desmond throws to first for a double play.

(continued on page 107)

Crane did some job. One pitch and he got two outs.

In the top of the ninth inning, the score is still Bombers 1, Terriers 0. The Terriers are coming up for their last shot. It has been five years since anyone else won a World Series. And you have a chance to stop the Terriers from setting a new consecutive Series victory record. You, Jerry Crane, and your defense.

The first batter flies out to left field. The second batter singles. The third man up lines out to center.

Pinch hitter Bobby Reynolds is walking up to the plate. Reynolds, finishing up a long and spectacular baseball career, is a good hitter. Crane will have to be careful.

The count goes to one and two. Crane could either waste a pitch or try to blow one by the hitter.

Marshall glances over to the dugout. You have to signal him what to do.

—To waste a pitch, turn to page 112.

—To go for the strikeout, turn to page 110.

"How's the hand feel?" you ask Marshall. "Not so good, Coach," he says.

There is no sense in leaving an injured player on the field. Not in a one-run game when a small mistake can make the difference.

You want Jamie Cross to run for Marshall. Maybe if you let Cross vent some of his energy on the base paths, he will not sing that horrible song anymore.

Roselli hits the next pitch into right field for a single. Cross scores easily. When he comes into the dugout, Billy Sawatski and Slick Desmond run out to greet him. Kid Costello comes up to them and the four begin to sing:

> "At bat, we hit off the best;
> On defense, we get out the rest. . . ."

No luck in stopping the song, but you are happy with a 2–0 lead.

The Terriers tie the game in the top of the eighth. You don't score in the bottom of the inning, and it is 2–2 going into the top of the ninth.

(continued on page 109)

The Terriers are challenging. With one out, they have a runner on third. A long fly ball will score the runner and put the Terriers ahead by a run. Hank Percy, the American League home-run champion, is the batter.

There are two ways to defense this situation. You can have your outfielders play back and come racing in on any fly ball hit in front of them. This gives them momentum going toward home plate and gives them a chance to throw out a runner trying to tag up on a medium-range fly ball. Or you could have your outfielders play in. This concedes a run on a medium fly, but gives you a chance to cut off a low line drive and then have a play at the plate if the runner tries to score.

—*To have your outfielders play back, turn to page 116.*

—*To have your outfielders play in, turn to page 114.*

Crane rears back and fires with all his might. A fastball with all the speed Crane's unrested arm can bring. Usually a Crane fastball is unhittable. But on two days' rest, there is something missing from this one. It lacks the zip and skip of a normal Crane heater.

Reynolds swings and strokes a ground ball toward third base. It should be an easy play for Sawatski. But at the last second, the ball hits something and leaps into the air. Sawatski reaches up for the ball but not high enough. It skips into left field for a bad-hop base hit.

With runners on first and second, Tony Mason rips a double off the wall in right field. Both runners score. Crane gets the next hitter to pop out. But the Terriers are ahead 2–1.

Al Whitcomb, pitching in relief for the Terriers, holds the Bombers scoreless in the bottom of the ninth.

It is a heartbreaking loss—to come so far and lose on a bad hop.

The End

You stay by the water cooler. That is the place you always stand. You look out onto the field. The Terriers look strong. The Bombers—just waving at the ball—are up at the plate. You are frustrated and you are mad.

Moose Harrington strikes out.

You look up at the scoreboard. It tells the whole story. You are losing 5–0 in the ninth inning and there are two out.

Billy Sawatski is up. He takes the first pitch for a strike. That is all you can handle. You throw your hat at the water cooler. You kick the water cooler. You punch it. Ouch, that hurt.

Shucks. You walk right out of the dugout. Out of the locker room. To your car in the parking lot. As you walk out, you hear a lot of cheering. It sounds like the Bombers are making a comeback. You think about turning around and going back into the ball park.

"Ah!" you say to yourself. "It's hopeless."

The Bombers might still win the World Series. But you gave up on your team. If the Cats do show a ninth life and win, you will not have had anything to do with it.

The End

Crane is way ahead of the batter. No sense in giving Reynolds a pitch he can handle. Crane winds up and tosses a fastball low and away. Reynolds holds back. The ball bounces in the dirt. Marshall jumps over and blocks the pitch with his chest.

When you saw the pitch bounce, your heart jumped a beat. Only a great defensive play by Marshall saved a wild pitch. That is why you left your gutsy, heads-up catcher in the game.

(continued on page 113)

The count goes full at 3–2. Ninth inning, two out, runner on first. You are ahead by one run. The tension is building.

"C'mon, Crane," you yell. The guys on the bench are cheering. The fans are clapping, clapping, clapping.

Reynolds digs in. Crane checks the runner, kicks, and delivers. A curve ball. Reynolds swings and misses. Strike three!

Marshall runs out to the mound. He hugs Crane and lifts the pitcher in the air. Players, fans, police—all crowd around the pitcher's mound.

You want to join the celebration. But first you have to speak to Terrier manager Art London.

You find him in the Terrier dugout.

"Good Series, Art. Your boys played well," you say,

"Thank you. Your team, too," he says.

You nod. It is hard to be modest when, inside, you are grinning ear to ear.

The End

If you are going to lose this game, it will be here and now. If Percy hits a long fly ball, the go-ahead run will score, and he will easily go into second with a double before your outfielders can retrieve the ball.

But if he hits a line drive, you are going to have a chance not only to rob him of a hit, but to throw out the runner if he dares attempt to tag up. That could provide an exhilarating turning point. If that happens, the Terriers would be demoralized and the Bombers would be all fired up.

It is a win-or-lose decision. You hope it comes out win.

You tap the water cooler with the pinky and thumb of your left hand. You did that once long ago and your hitter socked a home run. Ever since then, whenever you need good luck, you tap your thumb and pinky on the water cooler. You never needed luck as much as you do now.

(continued on page 115)

Luck is nice to have, but so is a good pitcher. You bring in Richard Roscoe. He throws two fastballs past Percy. Then he throws a change-up. Percy swings but is way ahead of the ball—strike three!

Brad Boysenberry is the next Terrier hitter. And the next Roscoe strikeout victim. Roscoe fans Boysenberry on a fastball timed at 101 miles per hour on the radar gun. That is fast.

And so is Jet Johnson. In the bottom of the ninth, Jet walks with two out. He steals second and then scores on a base hit by Skeets Rodriguez. You win 3–2.

What a team. What a season. What a victory!

The End

You are not ready to concede anything. If Percy hits a medium-range fly ball, you think that your outfielders can make a play at the plate close.

They are going to play back, and, if that runner on third wants to make a go for home, he will have to challenge your big guns in the outfield. Hank Percy comes up to bat. He is carrying three weighted bats along with his regular bat. That means he is going to try to get around on your fastball pitcher, reliever Richard Roscoe. No more of this trying-to-hit-to-left-field stuff for Percy. The mighty left-hander wants to match his power against Roscoe's fastball.

Percy drops the weighted bats one by one, taking a full cut first with three, then two, then one. That leaves only his regular bat. Time to do battle—bat versus ball.

(continued on page 118)

Roscoe is tough. He performs well in these high-pressure situations. But Percy is the best there is.

The first pitch is low. The next pitch is a fastball around the letters. Percy swings and hits it high into right field. The ball is not too deep and Skeets Rodriguez waits a second before coming in on the ball. He times his run so that he gets to the ball with a full head of steam toward the plate.

Skeets catches the ball and, in one motion, rears back and shoots a bullet toward home. The runner on third tags and gets a pretty good start. He is starting his slide as the ball arrives at the plate. Edwards grabs the ball, blocks the plate, and tags the runner sliding home.

He's out. What a double play. The score is still tied going into the bottom of the ninth.

Albert Edwards ends that quickly. The backup catcher hits a home run over Hank Percy's head in right field. The Terriers go home beaten by a run. You win the World Series.

Your dream has come true.

The End

ABOUT THE AUTHOR
& ILLUSTRATOR

MITCH GELMAN has played alongside and against some of America's top baseball stars. As a third-baseman for Los Angeles' Palisades High School in 1980, Mitch's opponents included Darryl Strawberry, who was selected by the New York Mets that year as Major League Baseball's number-one draft choice. In a Los Angeles winter-league club managed by San Francisco Giant superscout George Genovese, Mitch's teammates included Jack Clark, Gary Alexander, and other big leaguers. Mitch is currently a student at the University of California at Berkeley. He has written two other Archway Paperbacks—*Can You Win the Pennant?* and *Pro Football Showdown*—and has worked as a reporter for *Time* magazine and the Los Angeles *Herald-Examiner*.

With thirty years of experience behind him, AL FIORENTINO is a very versatile and talented artist. After graduating from the Philadelphia College of Art, he worked as an advertising illustrator. Since then, he has also worked in book illustration and painting. He never limits himself to a specific area, but instead enjoys doing everything from portraits and landscapes to animals and sports players! Mr. Fiorentino's studio is located in Yardley, Pennsylvania, and he lives nearby with his wife, who is an art teacher.